Usborne English

Level 2

The Little Mermaid

Retold by Mairi Mackinnon

Illustrated by Elena Selivanova

English language consultant: Peter Viney

Contents

You can listen to the story online here:
www.usborneenglishreaders.com/
littlemermaid

Far out to sea, deep under water is the Sea King's country. Some people think there is only sand and rock at the bottom of the sea, but it's a beautiful place. Graceful plants grow there like the trees and flowers on land. Bright silver fish swim through them, like birds in the air. The Sea King's palace is in the middle of an underwater forest, and fish swim in and out of the open windows.

The Sea King had six pretty mermaid daughters. When they were young, they used to play in the palace gardens, and each mermaid princess made her own little garden. One filled her garden with red sea flowers, another made pictures with shells, and another used beautiful round stones.

After a ship sank, the youngest princess found a stone statue of a boy.

She put the statue in her garden, with tall sea plants all around it. She used to sit there for hours, and she wondered about the world above the sea.

Her grandmother told her stories. "The people there are very strange. They don't have fish tails, like us, but two things called legs. They can't swim very well, so they cross the sea in ships. Sometimes they live together in towns and cities. When you are sixteen years old, you can swim up to the surface of the sea and see all these things."

Soon after that, the oldest princess had her sixteenth birthday, and there was a wonderful party in the palace. There was music and dancing all night. At the end of the party, the youngest princess sang. The little mermaid had the sweetest voice. Everyone smiled when they heard her.

The next day, the oldest princess swam up
to the sea surface. When she came back,
her sisters asked, "What was it like?"

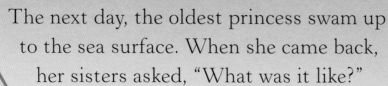

"It was beautiful," said the
oldest princess. "I saw a city!"
She told them about the buildings,
the people in the busy streets and the
bright evening lights in all the windows.
   "Oh, I'd like to see that," said the little
mermaid.

The next year, the second princess swam to the surface. "I saw a ship!" she told her sisters. "There was a party, and everyone was wearing beautiful clothes. They had music, and lights all around the ship at night, and they were dancing and talking and laughing."

Each year, another princess swam up to
the world above. They came back and told
stories of snowy mountains, green hills and
dark forests. They saw animals in the fields,
children playing by the water, and ships
and boats out at sea. Everything was new
and strange for them. The little
mermaid listened to
their stories again
and again.

At last the little mermaid was sixteen,
and she could swim to the surface.
It was a calm evening and the sea was quite
flat, with no waves. Soon she saw a ship. She
remembered her sister's story and swam closer.

On this ship they were having a party too,
with lights and music. Someone came to
the side of the ship and looked out to sea,
although he didn't see the little mermaid
down below.

He was young and handsome, and he was
wearing a gold crown.

"So he's a prince," she thought. "He looks
like the statue in my garden."

Someone shouted, "Happy Birthday, sir!"
and suddenly the sky was full of fireworks.
The little mermaid was frightened by the
noise, but then she saw all the silver and
gold and red and purple stars in the sky.
"Oh, they're beautiful!" she thought.

The sea wasn't so calm now. A storm was coming. The air was full of wind and rain, and soon the waves were as high as mountains.

The people on the ship were frightened, and the little mermaid was frightened for them. Then one enormous wave went over the ship, and it began to sink under the waves.

The little mermaid looked around and
saw the prince. He was trying to swim in the
cold water, but he couldn't do it. He stopped
moving and closed his eyes. The little
mermaid put her arms around him and lifted
his head above the surface, and the waves
carried them far away from the shipwreck.

The next morning, the sun was shining and she could see the land. The little mermaid was still holding the prince. She swam to the shore and pulled him out of the water. She could just see a large white building, and she could hear voices. She swam behind some rocks, and watched.

Soon some girls came down to the shore, and saw the prince on the sand. One pretty girl sat down beside him and touched his face. The prince opened his eyes and smiled.

"He doesn't know about me," thought the little mermaid. "He doesn't know that I saved his life." She swam back to her father's castle under the sea, but she couldn't be happy. She stayed in her sea garden for hours, and looked at her statue and remembered the prince.

"Little sister, why are you so sad?" asked the other mermaids. She told them about the prince and the shipwreck.

"I've seen him, I'm sure," said her oldest sister. "He lives in a palace in the city by the sea. Come with us, and we'll swim there together." The six mermaids swam up to the city. Someone in the palace opened a window and looked out to sea.

"That's him, that's my prince!" said the little mermaid. "Do you think he's looking for me?" But she didn't really believe it.

Often after that, the little mermaid swam to the city and watched the palace. She didn't see the prince again, but people in the city often talked about him. Everyone loved the handsome young prince – he was so good and kind, they said.

"Can a mermaid ever change into a human?" the little mermaid asked one day.

"Change into a human? Why?" her grandmother said. "Mermaids live for hundreds of years. We have graceful fish tails and beautiful voices. Humans have ugly legs and they have short, sad lives. It is possible to become a human, but it's very dangerous. Only the Sea Witch can change you, and she asks a terrible price. Stay with us and be happy, little one. Forget about your prince."

But the little mermaid couldn't forget
him. Later, she swam quietly away from
the palace to where the sea was darkest and
deepest. There was nothing graceful here.
Sea snakes grew out of the ground, like
living plants with wide, hungry mouths. All
around them were hundreds of white human
bones. The Sea Witch lived in a house in
the middle. Her house was made of bones.
The little mermaid was very frightened,
but she swam quickly
between the snakes to
the bone house.

The Sea Witch was old and very ugly. She had thick red hair, and purple snakes swam all over her body. "I know what you want," she said, "but it won't make you happy. I will make a magic drink for you, and you must go up to the shore and drink it. You will lose your fish tail, and you'll have two legs instead. Everyone will say you are beautiful and graceful, but when you walk, you will think you are walking on sharp knives." She laughed horribly.

"I will do that," said the little mermaid.

"You can never come back to your father's palace and your sisters under the sea.

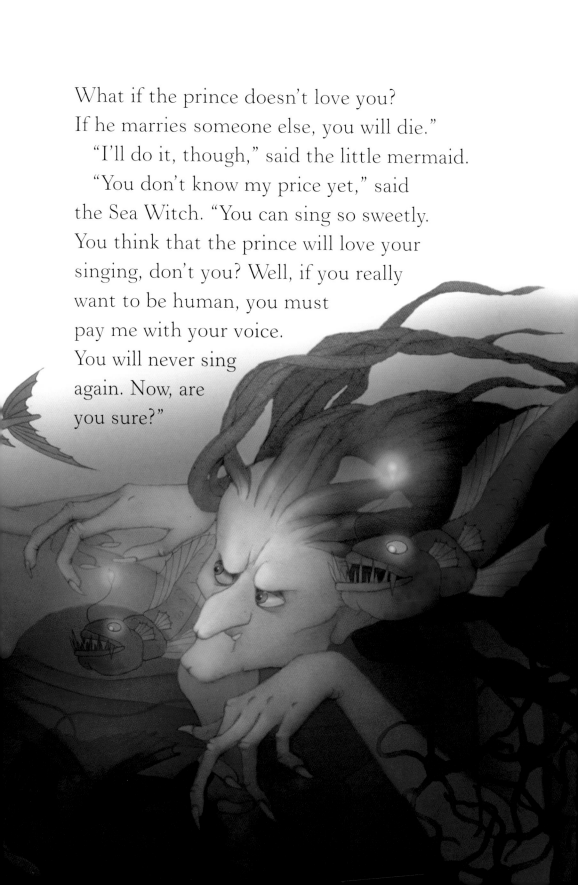

What if the prince doesn't love you?
If he marries someone else, you will die."

"I'll do it, though," said the little mermaid.

"You don't know my price yet," said
the Sea Witch. "You can sing so sweetly.
You think that the prince will love your
singing, don't you? Well, if you really
want to be human, you must
pay me with your voice.
You will never sing
again. Now, are
you sure?"

The little mermaid went pale, but she said, "I'm sure." Those were the last words she ever spoke. Then the Sea Witch began making the magic drink, and the little mermaid watched with wide, frightened eyes. At last the Sea Witch gave her a small black bottle.

"There! What are you waiting for?" she said in the little mermaid's voice, and she laughed even more.

The little mermaid swam away quickly.
She swam past the palace, but she didn't
stop. She couldn't speak to her sisters and
her father and her grandmother now. She
couldn't say goodbye to them. She swam up
to the sea surface and to the prince's palace.
She pulled herself out of the water onto
some stone steps, and then she drank from
the black bottle. She felt a terrible pain, but
when she looked down, her fish tail was
gone and she had
two human legs.

"Who are you? What has happened to you?"

The little mermaid looked up. It was her prince! She felt so happy, but she couldn't speak to him.

The prince called to his servants. "Quickly, bring some clothes for this young lady." The servants helped her to get dressed, and then she tried to stand up. Her legs and feet hurt terribly, but she didn't mind. The prince was beside her.

"You remind me of someone in a country far away," said the prince. "She saved my life after a shipwreck. I never saw her again."

"That was me!" thought the little mermaid, but she couldn't say anything.

Everyone who saw her said, "She's so pretty, so graceful. It's such a pity that she can't speak."

She followed the prince everywhere. "My dear sweet friend," he called her. She used to sit beside him and watch him for hours. "You can almost speak with your eyes," he said. "I think you love me more than anyone." When she walked, the pain was still terrible, but she never cried.

Sometimes, at night, she used to sit by the sea and wash her feet in the cold water. Sometimes her sisters swam close to the palace. "Little one, we miss you so much," they said. She smiled to show them that she was happy, but she missed them too.

"Dear friend," the prince said one day. "You know, my father wants me to marry a princess. They say she is very beautiful and kind, but I don't want to marry someone I've never met. I'd like to marry you, but of course I have to listen to my father. I should go and meet her, at least. Will you come with me?" The little mermaid smiled, but she felt so sad. Her heart was breaking.

They sailed away from the city. The little mermaid
looked down into the deep blue-green water. Was that
her father's palace, far below? At night, she heard
sad mermaid songs. Her sisters
were singing to her. At last
they reached the city in
the south where the
princess lived.

"Oh, little friend, it's her!" said the prince. "That's the girl who saved me – I know it is! I remember her so well. Can you believe it? I know you'll be happy for me. We can be married tomorrow!"

It was true. The little mermaid recognized the pretty girl from the shore after the shipwreck. So she was a princess, too.

That night, there was a wonderful party.
The prince and princess danced for hours.
They were deeply in love already. The little
mermaid danced and smiled, too, but soon
she left the party. Then she ran down to
the sea, and cried and cried. She could hear
music from the palace. Later there were
fireworks, and she remembered the night of
the shipwreck.

"Little one!" She looked up and saw five heads above the water. "The Sea Witch told us about your prince. Come back to us, little sister. Come and swim with us for one more night." The little mermaid jumped into the water and her sisters put their arms around her. Then they all swam together, far out to sea in the moonlight.

About Hans Christian Andersen

Hans Christian Andersen was born in Denmark over 100 years ago. When he was just 14, he left home to become an actor. When it was hard to find acting work, he started writing.

Andersen loved to travel, and went to lots of European countries. He wrote about the things he saw and the people he met. His travel books were popular, but his most famous books are the stories he wrote for children, including *The Emperor's New Clothes, The Snow Queen* and *The Ugly Duckling.*

The Little Mermaid is one of Andersen's most popular stories today. In the story, the little mermaid had a statue of a prince. Now Andersen's home city of Copenhagen has a famous statue of... The Little Mermaid.

Activities

The answers are on page 40.

The people in the story

Choose *two* sentences for each person.

The little mermaid...   The prince...   The princess...   The Sea Witch...

A.
...finds a stone statue after a shipwreck.

B.
...sees the prince on the sand.

C.
...is old and very ugly.

D.
...is young and handsome.

E.
...dances with the prince for hours.

F.
...has the sweetest voice.

G.
...lives in a house made of bones.

H.
...doesn't want to marry someone he's never met.

Mixed-up story

Can you put these pictures and sentences in order?

A.

"Come back to us, little sister. Come and swim with us for one more night."

B.

The little mermaid danced and smiled, too, but soon she left the party.

C.

Later, she swam quietly away to where the sea was darkest and deepest.

D.

"You remind me of someone in a country far away," said the prince.

E.

"Will you come with me?" The little mermaid smiled, but she felt so sad.

F.

Her fish tail was gone and she had two human legs.

G.

"I know what you want," said the Sea Witch, "but it won't make you happy."

H.

"That's him, that's my prince!" said the little mermaid.

I.

"Oh, little friend!" said the prince. "That's the girl who saved me."

Under water and on land

Choose the right sentence for each picture.

1.

A. Her grandmother
   told her secrets.

B. Her grandmother
   told her stories.

2.

A. Each year, another princess
   swam up to the world above.

B. Each year, another princess
   swam up to the sky above.

3.

A. Often after that, the little
   mermaid swam to the city
   and watched the palace.

B. Often after that, the little
   mermaid swam to the city
   and helped the people.

4.

A. She felt so shy that she
   couldn't speak to him.

B. She felt so happy, but she
   couldn't speak to him.

The prince in danger
Which three things *can't* you see in the picture?

ship   moon   sea

prince   storm   sky

rain   waves   mermaid

Where are they? Where are they going?

Choose the right word to finish each sentence.

1.

There was a wonderful
party ..... the palace.

2.

The next day, the oldest
princess swam ..... to the
sea's surface.

by

into

3.

Soon some girls came
down to the shore, and saw
the prince ..... the sand.

4.

He lives in a palace in the
city ..... the sea

up

in

5.

Was that her father's
palace, far .....?

6.

The little mermaid
jumped ..... the water.

below

on

Word list

bone (n) your bones are the hard white parts inside your body. Bones give your body its shape.

building (n) houses are buildings. There are lots of buildings in a town or city.

calm (adj) if something is calm, it is quiet and peaceful, not stormy.

crown (n) kings, queens, princes and princesses wear crowns on their heads. They are usually made of gold and precious stones.

fireworks (n pl) you often see fireworks in the sky at parties and on special days. They make bright light and loud noises.

graceful (adj) when something is graceful, it moves beautifully.

human (n, adj) a person is human. Animals and plants are not human.

lady (n) a polite word for a woman.

lift (v) when you lift something, you move or carry it to a higher place.

mermaid (n) an imaginary creature that has a woman's head and body and a fish's tail.

pain (n) when something hurts you, you feel pain.

price (n) how much something costs.

remind (v) when something reminds you, it makes you think of someone, something or somewhere you knew in the past.

sail (v) when a boat travels from one place to another, it sails.

sand (n) you find sand by the sea. It is a thin, soft powder made of rock.

servant (n) someone who works for another person, especially in their home.

sharp (adj) if something is sharp, it can cut you or hurt you.

shipwreck (n) when a ship hits a rock and breaks apart or sinks, it is a shipwreck.

shore (n) the land beside a river, lake or sea.

sink, sank (v) when something sinks into water, it goes down under the water and rests at the bottom.

statue (n) a model of a person, made of stone or metal.

steps (n pl) steps are like stairs outside a building. They are often made of stone.

surface (n) the surface of the sea is the very top of the water, where it meets the air above.

sweet (adj) when something sounds sweet, it is beautiful to hear.

wave (n) when the surface of the sea is not completely calm and flat, it has waves. Waves are bigger when there is a strong wind or a storm.

Answers

The people in the story
The little mermaid: A, F
The prince: D, H
The princess: B, E
The Sea Witch: C, G

Mixed-up story
H, C, G, F, D,
E, I, B, A

Under water and on land
1. B
2. A
3. A
4. B

The prince in danger
moon
prince
mermaid

Where are they?
Where are they going?
1. in
2. up
3. on
4. by
5. below
6. into

You can find information about
other Usborne English Readers here:
www.usborneenglishreaders.com

Designed by Jodie Smith

Series designer: Laura Nelson Norris

Edited by Jane Chisholm

With thanks to Laura Cowan

Digital imaging: John Russell

Page 32: picture of Hans Christian Anderson © The Granger Collection/Topfoto
Picture of Little Mermaid © ullstein bild/Getty Images

First published in 2018 by Usborne Publishing Ltd.,
Usborne House, 83-85 Saffron Hill, London EC1N 8RT, England.
www.usborne.com Copyright © 2018 Usborne Publishing Ltd.